A Fox u

Moonlig

a poetry anthology
selected by

Morag Styles

Contents

Why I Came

When I walked into this deep little wood,
I didn't know why I came;
Until an owl flew by,
And softly called my name.

John Cunliffe

No Rain, No Rainbow

Suppose today
you're feeling down
your face propping a frown

Suppose today
you're one streak of a shadow
the sky giving you a headache

Tomorrow
you never know
you might wake up
in the peak of a glow.

If you don't get the rain
how can you get the rainbow?

Say it again, Granny,
No rain, no rainbow.

Say it again, Granny,
No rain, no rainbow.

John Agard

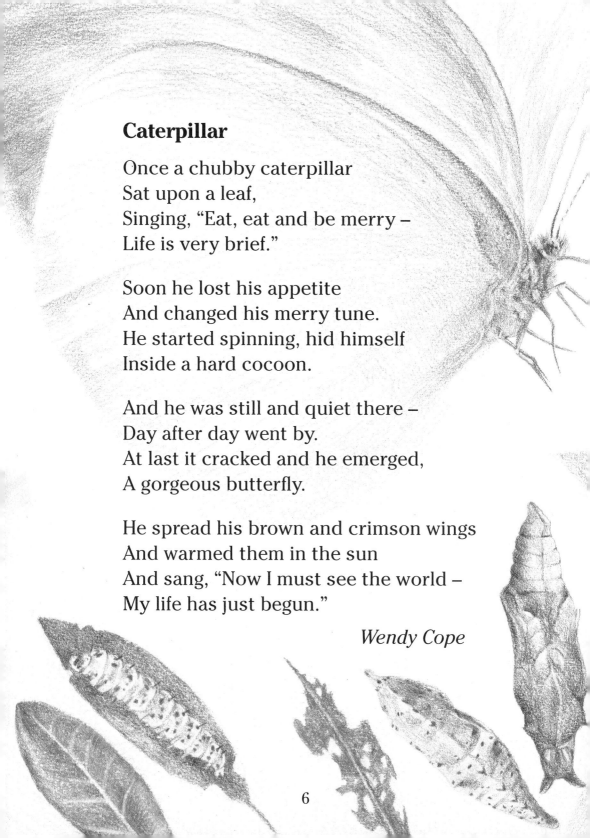

Caterpillar

Once a chubby caterpillar
Sat upon a leaf,
Singing, "Eat, eat and be merry –
Life is very brief."

Soon he lost his appetite
And changed his merry tune.
He started spinning, hid himself
Inside a hard cocoon.

And he was still and quiet there –
Day after day went by.
At last it cracked and he emerged,
A gorgeous butterfly.

He spread his brown and crimson wings
And warmed them in the sun
And sang, "Now I must see the world –
My life has just begun."

Wendy Cope

Butterfly Tongues

We wouldn't need straws for bottles,
we wouldn't need straws to drink,
if we had tongues like butterflies
we'd never need straws, I think.

If we had tongues uncoiling
like tubes without a kink,
we could sip way down like butterflies
when we wanted a way-down drink.

Aileen Fisher

A Dragonfly

When the heat of the summer
Made drowsy the land,
A dragonfly came
And sat on my hand,
With its blue jointed body,
And wings like spun glass,
It lit on my fingers
As though they were grass.

Eleanor Farjeon

Where innocent bright-eyed daisies are,
With blades of grass between,
Each daisy stands up like a star
Out of a sky of green.

Christina Rossetti

Daisies

The stars are everywhere tonight,
Above, beneath me and around;
They fill the sky with powdery light
And glimmer from the night-strewn ground;
For where the folded daisies are
In every one I see a star.

And so I know that when I pass
Where no sun's shadow counts the hours
And where the sky was there is grass
And where the stars were there are flowers,
Through the long night in which I lie
Stars will be shining in my sky.

Andrew Young

Escape at Bedtime

The lights from the parlour and kitchen shone out
　　Through the blinds and the windows and bars;
And high overhead and all moving about,
　　There were thousands of millions of stars.
There ne'er were such thousands of leaves on a tree,
　　Nor of people in church or the Park,
As the crowds of the stars that looked down upon me,
And that glittered and winked in the dark.

The Dog, and the Plough, and the Hunter, and all,
　　And the star of the sailor, and Mars,
These shone in the sky, and the pail by the wall
　　Would be half full of water and stars.
They saw me at last, and they chased me with cries,
　　And they soon had me packed into bed;
But the glory kept shining and bright in my eyes,
　　And the stars going round in my head.

R. L. Stevenson

How Many Stars?

When I was a boy
I would ask my dad:
"How many stars are there hanging in the sky?"
"More than enough, son,
More than I could say.
Enough to keep you counting
Till your dying day."

When I was a boy
I would ask my dad:
"How many fishes are there swimming in the sea?"
"More than enough, son,
More than I could say.
Enough to keep you counting
Till your dying day."

When I was a boy
I would ask my dad:
"How many creepy-crawlies are there in the world?"
"More than enough, son,
More than I could say.
Enough to keep you counting
Till your dying day."

Colin McNaughton

The Midnight Fox

When the night is young
And is waiting to be used,
To be blown, to be sounded,
The orange fox with moonlight eyes
Prowls,
Snooping, with nostrils quivering
As the wind disturbs quiet smells that hide in the
cloak of the shadows,
And he smiles.

Michael Duggan (12)

Silver

Slowly, silently, now the moon
Walks the night in her silver shoon;
This way, and that, she peers, and sees
Silver fruit upon silver trees;
One by one the casements catch
Her beams beneath the silvery thatch;
Couched in his kennel, like a log,
With paws of silver sleeps the dog;
From their shadowy cote the white breasts peep
Of doves in a silver-feathered sleep;
A harvest mouse goes scampering by,
With silver claws, and silver eye;
And moveless fish in the water gleam,
By silver reeds in a silver stream.

Walter de la Mare

Feeding the Cats

"I'll give this gravy to the cats,"
    I heard my mother say
in the dark outside the kitchen door;
    but the gravy went astray;
the scrubbing brush she spilt it on
    got up and walked away.

"I hope it's got some friends," Mum said,
    "or perhaps some babies, who
can get their tongues between the prickles –
    a tricky thing to do
In future when I feed the cats
    I'll feed the hedgehogs too."
                            Fleur Adcock

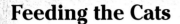

I never knew

I never knew
a crown of thorns
could curl itself
into a ball

I never knew
a hairbrush
could breathe in
and out

I never knew
a nest of needles
could sprout
a beady nose
and actually move

Not until I lifted
that old carpet
beside the garden shed
and met HEDGEHOG
my bristling brother.

John Agard

Hare

Son of the little dark-brown one with spots,
Little yellow one, leaper from the stubble,
Yonder is the son of the little dark-brown one,
Leaper from the treeless plain,
Leaper from the trunks of trees,
He leaps up, stiffens his tail,
And puts his ears back on his shoulders.

Traditional African

Small, Smaller

I thought that I knew all there was to know
Of being small, until I saw, black against the snow,
A shrew, trapped in my footprint, jump and fall
And jump again and fall, the hole too deep, the walls too tall.

Russell Hoban

Roger the Dog

Asleep he wheezes at his ease.
He only wakes to scratch his fleas.

He hogs the fire, he bakes his head
As if it were a loaf of bread.

He's just a sack of snoring dog.
You can lug him like a log.

You can roll him with your foot.
He'll stay snoring where he's put.

Take him out for exercise
He'll roll in cowclap up to his eyes.

He will not race, he will not romp.
He saves his strength for gobble and chomp.

He'll work as hard as you could wish
Emptying the dinner dish,

Then flops flat, and digs down deep,
Like a miner, into sleep.

Ted Hughes

Pussy In De Moonlight

Pussy in de moonlight
Pussy in de zoo
Pussy never come home
Till half past two

Traditional Caribbean

The Dark

I don't like the dark coming down on my head
It feels like a blanket thrown over the bed
I don't like the dark coming down on my head

I don't like the dark coming down over me
It feels like the room's full of things I can't see
I don't like the dark coming down over me

There isn't enough light from under the door
It only just reaches the edge of the floor
There isn't enough light from under the door

I wish that my dad hadn't put out the light
It feels like there's something that's just out of sight
I wish that my dad hadn't put out the light

But under the bedclothes it's warm and secure
You can't see the ceiling you can't see the floor
Yes, under the bedclothes it's warm and secure
So I think I'll stay here till it's daylight once more.

Adrian Henri

Early in the Morning

Early in the morning
The water hits the rocks,
The birds are making noises
Like old alarum clocks,
The soldier on the skyline
Fires a golden gun
And over the back of the chimney-stack
Explodes the silent sun.

Charles Causley

Sun, Moon, Stars

Sun, moon, stars,
You that move in the heavens,
Hear this mother!
A new life has come among you.
Make its life smooth.

Native American oral tradition

23

Green Jewels

Suppose all the children
In the world turned green,
Green eyes, green hair, green colour!
Speaking in green voices everywhere;
The trees would be their mothers,
Summer would be their fathers,
And every night before they go to sleep
A black-eyed fairy will reap
Raindrops from their dreams
To keep them fresh and clean.

Faustin Charles

Who Dat Girl?

Who dat wide-eye likkle girl
Staring out at me?
Wid her hair in beads an' braids
An' skin like ebony?

Who dat girl, her eye dem bright
Like night-time peeny-wallie?
Wid Granny chain dem circle roun'
Her ankle, neck, an' knee?

Who dat girl in Mummy's shoes,
Waist tie wid Dad's hankie?
Who dat girl wid teeth like pearl
Who grinning out at me?

Who dat girl? Who dat girl?
Pretty as poetry?
Who dat girl in de lookin'-glass?

Yuh mean dat girl is me?

Valerie Bloom

When I grow up

When I grow up
What shall I be?
Will I be different
Or still be me?

Michelle Magorian

How I See It

Some say the world's
A hopeless case:
A speck of dust
In all that space.
It's certainly
A scruffy place.
Just one hope
For the human race
That I can see:
Me. I'm
ACE!

Kit Wright

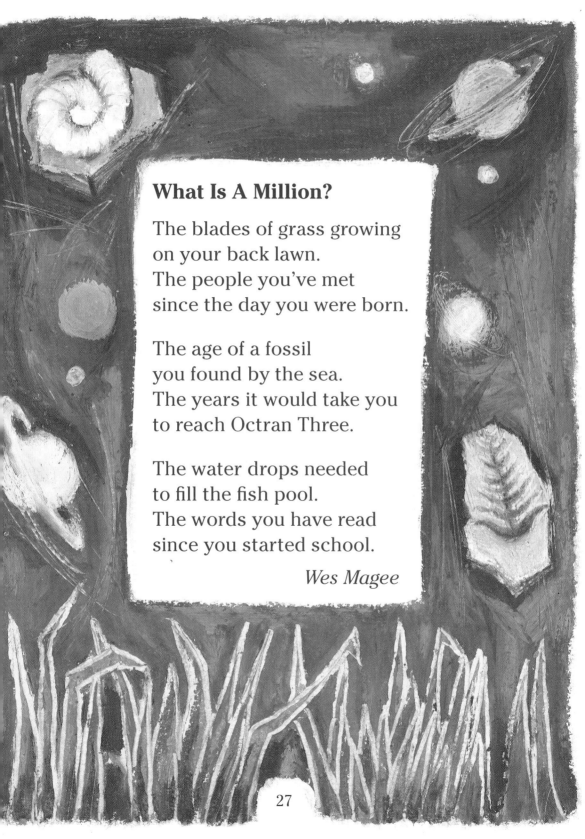

What Is A Million?

The blades of grass growing
on your back lawn.
The people you've met
since the day you were born.

The age of a fossil
you found by the sea.
The years it would take you
to reach Octran Three.

The water drops needed
to fill the fish pool.
The words you have read
since you started school.

Wes Magee

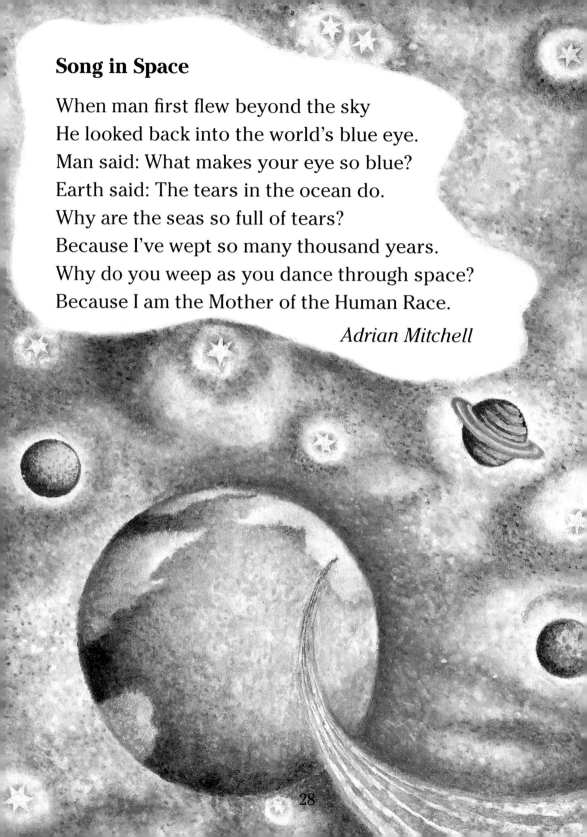

Song in Space

When man first flew beyond the sky
He looked back into the world's blue eye.
Man said: What makes your eye so blue?
Earth said: The tears in the ocean do.
Why are the seas so full of tears?
Because I've wept so many thousand years.
Why do you weep as you dance through space?
Because I am the Mother of the Human Race.

Adrian Mitchell

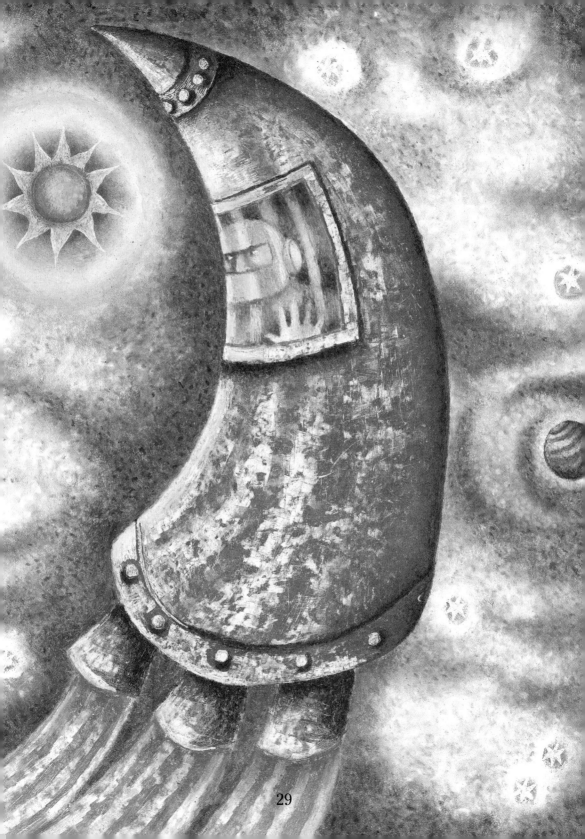

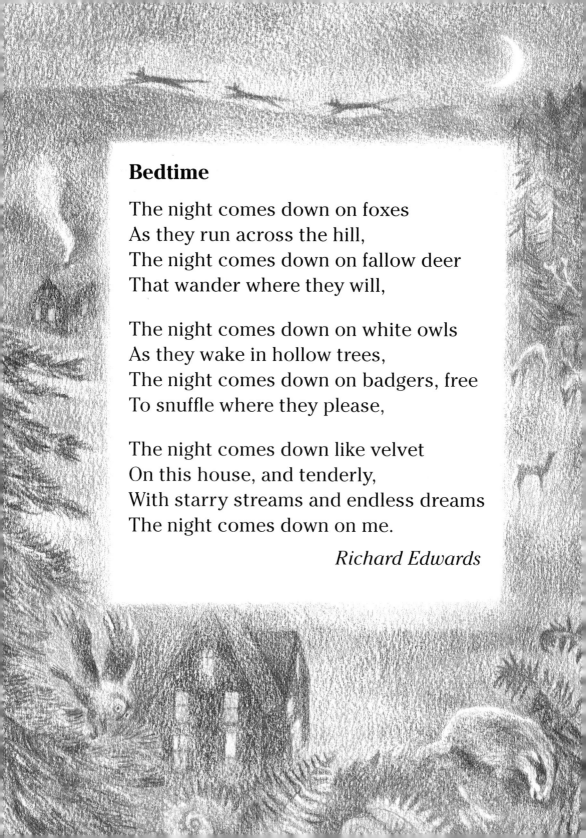

Bedtime

The night comes down on foxes
As they run across the hill,
The night comes down on fallow deer
That wander where they will,

The night comes down on white owls
As they wake in hollow trees,
The night comes down on badgers, free
To snuffle where they please,

The night comes down like velvet
On this house, and tenderly,
With starry streams and endless dreams
The night comes down on me.

Richard Edwards

Index of Authors